Nature's Niagara

A Walk on the Wild Side

Dayna,

Best wishes,

Paul Gromosiak

Written and Illustrated by

PAUL GROMOSIAK

© 2000

Cover Concept: John Hardiman

Illustration Assistance: David Tyler Harnden

2

©2000 **Western New York Wares Inc.**
All rights reserved.
Printed by Petit Printing
Typesetting by Type Plus

Address all inquiries to:
Brian Meyer, Publisher
Western New York Wares Inc.
P.O. Box 733
Ellicott Station
Buffalo, NY 14205
(716) 832-6088

This book was published and printed in Buffalo, NY
ISBN: 1-879201-31-3

**Visit our Internet Site at
www.wnybooks.com**

Contents

"Some vast despair, some grief divine,
Doth vigil keep,
Forever here, Before this shrine
The waters weep.

Methinks a God from some far sphere,
In sportive part,
In ages past wooed Nature here,
And broke her heart.

Robert Loveman, 1893

To my niece,
Susan E. Ghearing;
my nephews,
Michael A. Gromosiak and
Gregory G. Gromosiak;
my godchildren,
Karin E. Sage and
Adam M. Sage

Acknowledgments

This book would not have been possible without the assistance of the dedicated staffs of the Local History Department of the Niagara Falls (New York) Public Library and the Schoellkopf Geological Museum, as well as the New York State Parks Interpretive staff on Goat Island.

I also want to thank Parker E. Calkin, Richard J. Batt, Dennis M. Torok and the United States Army Corps of Engineers.

Introduction

"Whence hast thou thy beginning? Who supplies,
Age after age, thy unexhausted springs?
What power hath order'd, that, when all thy weight
Descends into the deep, the swollen waves
Rise not, and roll to overwhelm the earth?"

When the famous poet, Jose Maria Hereclia, asked these questions in 1830, the story of the natural history of Niagara Falls was just beginning to be written. Today, the story is still not complete, and perhaps it never will be.

What is known for certain is that the falls have moved about seven miles (eleven kilometers) south from the Niagara Escarpment since the end of the last ice age, creating a gorge and whirlpool which are worthy rivals. While receding, the falls left behind evidence of special and exciting conditions, such as other falls which dried up, a buried gorge partly cleaned out, the rebirth of an ancient waterfall, the creation of Goat Island and the draining of a nearby lake.

Read on and learn about nature's finest creation. The story, though it is unfinished, will reveal much of the glory of Niagara.

Publisher's Ponderings

Paul Gromosiak oozed ecotourism decades before ecotourism was "cool."

Photo by Matthew Pitts

"You don't need helicopters and other tacky tourism attractions to sell the Falls," I remember Paul saying during our first visit to Goat Island back in late 1980s. "Just look around you! It's a natural wonder! That's what we should be promoting!"

Visiting the Falls with Paul as your tour guide would be a lot like attending a Metallica concert with Mozart. While the ghost of the great Austrian composer might instantaneously recognize the musicians' raw potential, the recital would likely turn the spirit a paler shade of white.

Nature's Niagara: A Walk on the Wild Side has been on Paul's literary "to do" list for many years. It's fitting — and entirely coincidental — that we're introducing this book in the same season that state officials have seen the light.

The Pataki administration has outlined an ambitious plan for transforming the American falls into an ecotourism destination. The vision includes a seven-mile hiking trail along the spectacular Niagara Gorge that links the Falls with Artpark in Lewiston. There's also talk of turning the Schoellkopf Geological Museum into an interactive children's nature exhibit and virtual reality theater and transforming a century-old structure on Goat Island into an interpretive center.

Paul's latest book is a testament to the natural majesty of Niagara Falls. Prepare to embark on a exhilarating armchair journey into a land where ring billed gulls can be seen resting in the calm waters near First Sister Island and where skittish gray squirrels can be seen snacking beneath stately trees. You'll learn how glaciers left their indelible marks on the region and you'll read about the colorful rainbows that appear in the mist.

Nature's Niagara will introduce you to the park's wildflowers and wild animals, its ferns and fungi and its amazing geological history.

This is our company's sixth literary collaboration with Paul. Since 1989, we've sold well over 30,000 copies of his fine books on Niagara Falls. This is a benchmark that most regional authors can only dream of reaching.

Publishing a book requires the talents of many individuals. Our thanks to Michele Ratzel, our business manager, who has been a pivotal force in our regional publishing odyssey since 1991. Tom Connolly, our marketing associate, has been instrumental in helping to strengthen Western New York Wares Inc. as it marches into the new millennium.

John Hardiman and the entire staff at Petit Printing helped to shape the book you're holding right now, as did Dick Grajek at Type Plus.

On a personal note, I thank my parents, Bill and Jean Meyer, for helping to instill in me an appreciation for our region's wonderful attributes. These lifelong Buffalonians have always been quick to remind their children that Western New York is truly a special place.

Brian Meyer
June 2000

Chapter 1:

The Geography of the Niagara Region

"The curiosity permitted to travelers made me wish to visit the Niagara fall, which I had heard spoken of as a marvelous curiosity. I was one of three to go there. I examined this astonishing cataract which has the form of a crescent, a quarter of a league in extent. They give to it the height, according to common report, of 180 feet. It is the discharge of Lake Erie, and receives its waters, which it throws into the strait or river of Niagara, which then empties into Lake Ontario near Fort Niagara."

M. Bonnefons, 1753

Lake Erie, the Niagara River and Lake Ontario divide the Niagara Region into two parts: the Niagara Peninsula and Western New York. The geographical characteristics of the Niagara Peninsula and Western New York are both unique and shared.

Important Geographical Characteristics

1. **Latitude.** About 42° 20' North to 43° 20' North.

2. **Longitude.** About 78° 30' West to 79° 30' West.

3. **Lake Ontario.** It is normally about 245 feet (75 meters) above sea level. Because of the postglacial rebound of Earth's crust to the northeast, the western shore of the lake is rising about 1 foot (0.3 meter) a century.

   Like that of the other four Great Lakes, the bed of Lake Ontario was once a group of preglacial river valleys.

   When discussing its history from about 12,300 to 4,000 years ago (BP), Lake Ontario is referred to as "Lake Iroquois."

   The surface of Lake Ontario seldom freezes over in the winter. In the summer, the colder water at the lake bottom often "upwells" or rises to the surface, sometimes suddenly.

   Fishing by or on the lake is quite good, but environmentalists advise a limit on consumption because of an ongoing, but slowly improving pollution problem.

The Schoellkopf Geological Museum is a New York State interpretive facility relating the natural history of the Niagara Gorge and Falls. It is located just over 0.5 mile (0.8 kilometer) north of the American Falls.

The New York State Regional Park Interpretive Programs Office on Goat Island. It provides outreach parks programs on local natural history to groups and the general public, utilizing all of the regions 14 state parks.

The Niagara Region

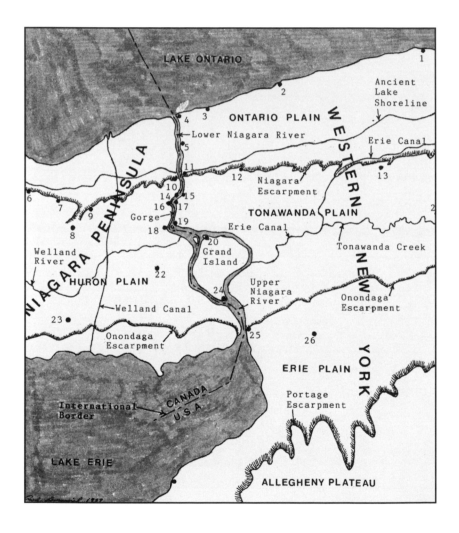

1. Golden Hill State Park

2. Wilson-Tuscarora State Park

3. Four Mile Creek State Campsite

4. Fort Niagara State Park

5. Joe Davis State Park

6. Balls Falls

7. Rockway Falls

8. Short Hills Provincial Park

9. Decew Falls

10. Queenston Heights Park; Trailhead of the Bruce Trail

11. Artpark

12. Bond Lake Park

13. Royalton Ravine Conservation Park

14. Niagara Glen Nature Reserve

15. Devil's Hole State Park

16. The Whirlpool; Buried St. David's Gorge

17. Whirlpool State Park

18. Queen Victoria Park; the Horseshoe (Canadian) Falls

19. Niagara Reservation State Park; the American and Bridal Veil Falls

20. Buckhorn Island State Park

21. Tonawanda Wildlife Management Area; Iroquois National Wildlife Refuge

22. Willoughby Marsh Conservation Area

23. Wainfleet Bog

24. Beaver Island State Park

25. Tifft Nature Preserve

26. Reinstein Woods State Unique Area

4. **The Border between Canada and The United States of America.** First established in 1796 at the center of the Niagara River, it was reestablished at the same location in 1819. Stone survey markers can be found along both sides of the river.

5. **The Ontario Plain.** This fertile land was part of the bed of Lake Iroquois (Ontario) from about 12,300 to 11,000 BP. The moderating effects of the lake during the winter and summer make the Ontario Plain an ideal location for orchards and vineyards.

6. **The Ancient Lake Shoreline.** This was the shoreline of Lake Iroquois (Ontario) from about 12,300 to 11,000 BP. Cobblestones from this postglacial beach have been used to build many houses and other structures in the Niagara Region.

7. **The Niagara Escarpment.** In the making for millions of years, this cliff runs south of Lake Ontario to Lake Huron. In the Niagara Peninsula, it is about 200 feet (61 meters) high. In Western New York, it is reaches about 250 feet (76 meters) at Lewiston. An escarpment is a cliff, often steep, created by an abrupt termination of gently inclined strata in the bedrock. The strata in the Niagara Region tilt about 20 feet (6 meters) every mile to the south.

   Because of layers of rocks of different hardness, the Niagara Escarpment actually has three cliffs in most places. These cliffs can best be seen at Artpark, in Lewiston, at the mouth of the Niagara River Gorge. At the top of the highest cliff is Lockport dolostone, a hard gray rock. The cliff further down is capped with Irondequoit and Reynales limestone, also hard and gray. The lowest cliff is capped with Whirlpool sandstone, gray but not as hard as the dolostone or limestone.

8. **The Lower Niagara River.** It meanders for about 7 miles (11 kilometers) from the mouth of the gorge to Lake Ontario. It is almost 100 feet (30 meters) deep at Lewiston/Queenston, and

from there to the lake the depth averages about 75 feet (23 meters). The fishing is great, but, for the same reasons as for Lake Ontario, limit consumption. There are boat docks at Lewiston, Youngstown and Niagara-on-the-Lake.

9. **The Niagara River Gorge.** It is about 7.1 miles (11 kilometers) long. Its height from Lewiston/Queenston to the Horseshoe Falls goes from about 300 feet (91 meters) to about 200 feet (61 meters). The river in the gorge ranges in depth from a few inches (about 8 centimeters) to 215 feet (66 meters).

10. **The Falls.** The heights of the Horseshoe (Canadian), American and Bridal Veil Falls vary with changes in the flow of the upper Niagara River. When the flow decreases, the level of the river in the gorge drops, increasing the height of the falls. The natural height of the Horseshoe or Canadian Falls is about 155 feet (47 meters). The natural height of the American and Bridal Veil Falls is about 170 feet (52 meters).

Since 50 to 75 percent of the water is diverted above the falls and sent to hydroelectric power plants, the heights of the falls are higher than normal all of the time. When 50 percent of the water is diverted during the daylight hours of the summer tourist season, the height of the Horseshoe Falls is about 170 feet (52 meters); the height of the American and Bridal Veil Falls is about 185 feet (56 meters). When 75 percent of the water is diverted the rest of the time, the height of the Horseshoe Falls is about 180 feet (55 meters); the height of the American and Bridal Veil Falls is about 195 feet (59 meters).

The natural flow of water over the Horseshoe Falls averages about 186,000 cubic feet per second (CFS) or 4,310 cubic meters per second (CMS). The natural flow over the American and Bridal Veil Falls averages about 20,000 CFS (566 CMS).

When 50 percent of the water is diverted, the flow of water over the Horseshoe Falls is always 90,000 CFS (2,549 CMS); the flow of water over the American and Bridal Veil Falls is 10,000 CFS (283 CMS). When 75 percent of the water is diverted, the flow of water over the Horseshoe Falls is 42,000 CFS (1,189 CMS); the flow of water over the American and Bridal Veil Falls is 8,000 CFS (227 CMS).

The Horseshoe Falls is about 1,000 feet (305 meters) wide, and the length of its crest line is about 2,500 feet (762 meters). The American Falls is about 900 feet (274 meters) wide, and the length of its crest line is about 1,100 feet (335 meters). The Bridal Veil Falls is about 40 feet (12 meters) wide.

11. **The Tonawanda Plain (The Huron Plain in Canada).** From about 12,300 to 3,500 BP, much of this area was flooded, forming shallow lakes of ever changing dimensions. The Lake on the Tonawanda Plain is called Lake Tonawanda; the Lake on the Huron Plain is called Lake Wainfleet. Both plains are bordered by the Niagara Escarpment on the north and the Onondaga Escarpment on the south.

12. **Grand Island.** This, the largest island in the Niagara River, splits the river into two channels: the western or Chippewa Channel and the Eastern or Tonawanda Channel. The Tonawanda Channel is about 3 miles (5 kilometers) longer.

About 27 square miles (70 square kilometers) in area, Grand Island is relatively flat and was once covered with an oak forest which was cleared for its excellent wood by colonial powers and the United States.

13. **The Welland Canal.** First opened in 1829, it was enlarged and relocated in 1845, 1887 and 1932. It is about 26 miles (42 kilometers) long and cuts across the Niagara Peninsula from Lake Erie to Lake Ontario. It is part of the 2,300 mile (3,700 kilometer)-long St. Lawrence Seaway, allowing ocean-going vessels to travel from the Atlantic Ocean to all of the five Great Lakes.

14. **The Erie Canal.** From 1825 until the arrival of the railroads in the 1840's, the Erie Canal was the most popular way to trans-

Lake Tonawanda and Lake Wainfleet

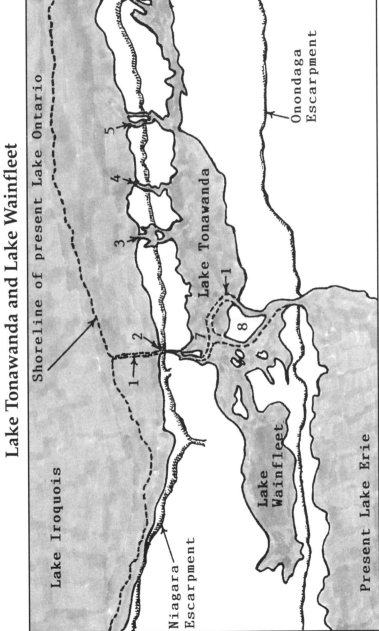

1. Present Niagara River
2. Lewiston Outlet
3. Lockport Outlet
4. Gasport Outlet
5. Medina Outlet
6. Holly Outlet
7. Niagara Island
8. Grand Island

port goods to and from the Hudson River and Lake Erie. Even though it was enlarged a little in 1918, its use declined greatly in the 20th century. Today, it is used by pleasure craft, and its towpaths are used by hikers and bicyclists.

15. **The Niagara River, in General.** Really a strait, it is 33 to 36 miles (53 to 58 kilometers) long, and it flows to the north from Lake Erie to Lake Ontario. Its width varies from about 250 feet (76 meters) at the Niagara Glen to about 8,500 feet (2,591 meters) at its source, the south end of Grand Island and at Navy Island. The Canadian side is mostly parkland, while the American side is mostly developed.

16. **The Upper Niagara River.** Going from Buffalo to the brinks of the falls, this part of the Niagara River is 19 to 22 miles (31 to 35 kilometers) long, depending upon which channel around Grand Island is used. The maximum depth in the upper river is about 41 feet (12 meters) near the International Railroad Bridge, at Buffalo.

    Nearly all the islands and islets in the Niagara River are in its upper portion, and some of them can only be seen when the river is low. Grand Island and Navy Island are the largest islands.

17. **The Onondaga Escarpment.** This is a limestone cliff about 10 feet (3 meters) high running east and west through the Niagara Peninsula and Western New York. In most places, it is hardly noticeable.

18. **Lake Erie.** Averaging about 572 feet (174 meters) above sea level, it is the shallowest of the Great Lakes, and this makes it possible for it to warm up and cool off faster than the other lakes.

    In the winter, Lake Erie usually forms a fairly thick sheet of ice on its surface. When the ice breaks up, it floats down the Niagara River to the falls where, in the past, it often dammed up the American Rapids and stopped the American and Bridal Veil Falls. Most of the ice, however, usually goes over the falls, especially the Horseshoe Falls, forming temporary bridges of ice in the gorge.

19. **The Erie Plain.** Once under a much larger postglacial Lake Erie, its soil is fertile, allowing for many successful vineyards and orchards. It lies between the Onondaga Escarpment and the Portage Escarpment.

20. **The Portage Escarpment.** This limestone escarpment marks the boundary between the Erie Plain and the Allegheny (Appalachian) Plateau. Rising to a height of about 1,000 feet (305 meters), it was made by the process of erosion over a long period of time.

21. **The Allegheny Mountains.** Rising to a maximum height of 2,000 feet (610 meters), they were made by the erosion of the Allegheny Plateau for millions of years.

22. **The Climate.** It is temperate *and* temperamental. Positioned between Lakes Erie and Ontario, the Niagara Region's weather is moderated but often unpredictable. In the winter, for example, the snowbelts produced by colder air passing over the lakes can suddenly move, changing a sunny day into a raging blizzard.

23. **The Flow of Water from Lake Erie.** Lake Erie receives water from Lakes Huron, Michigan and Superior, as well as its own drainage basin. The amount of water received varies from as little as 114,000 cubic feet per second (3,228 meters per second) to as much as 268,000 cubic feet per second (7,589 meters per second).

Chapter 2:

The Islands in the Niagara River

Taylor's Island

In 1876, a man named Taylor fell into the Whirlpool Rapids and was washed to a small rock and sand island. He was rescued and the island was named after him. Except for this island and a few rocks here and there, the Niagara River below the falls has no other islands.

On April 24, 1881, someone threw a dog from the Lower Suspension Bridge (it was on the same site as today's Whirlpool Rapids Bridge). The poor creature survived the plunge and managed to make it to Taylor's Island.

It wasn't long before the canine Robinson Crusoe was noticed by people. Many rescue attempts were made, but the dog would not cooperate, perhaps realizing that *his* "best friend" could no longer be trusted.

For the next few months, food was sent down to the dog from the bridge, and crowds gathered to get a glimpse of the "sole monarch" of the island.

One day, the dog was gone, never to be seen again. Did it swim to safety? Did it die trying? The answer will never be known.

The Islands in the Canadian and American Rapids

Before the intervention of human beings, nature was slowly washing away the islands in the rapids above the falls, and some of them, such as Gull Island, an island at the brink of the Horseshoe Falls, have disappeared.

Today, there are many islands, isles, islets, and rocks in the rapids. Because of the diversion of 50 to 75 percent of the water above the falls to the reservoirs used by the hydroelectric power stations. The rapids have severely diminished the past 40 years, decreasing the erosion of the old islands, isles, islets, and rocks. In fact, many of them are increasing in size, and new ones are appearing.

Named Islands in the Canadian and American Rapids

1. **Goat Island.** This is the large island which divides the Horse-shoe Falls from the Bridal Veil Falls. Now about 70 acres (0.28 square kilometer) in area, it was purported in 1750 to have been much larger — at least 1,450 feet (442 meters) long.

   Like the other islands in the rapids, it has been preserved because of its slightly more resistant strata. It is made up of sands and gravels lying upon Lockport dolostone.

   Until about 3,500 years ago, Goat Island was under a much deeper upper Niagara River. As the level of the river fell, the island went from a wetland to a true island.

   The climate on Goat Island is affected quite a bit by the surrounding waters and mists, allowing plants to flourish better than on the mainland. This condition was even more evident when there was more water and mist in the environment.

   The soil on Goat Island gradually becomes more shallow from the gorge to the Dividing of the Waters, the Native American name for that part of the island where water from the upper Niagara River is split into two channels: one taking water to the American and Bridal Veil Falls, and the other taking water to the Horseshoe Falls. Efforts to stem erosion along the island's shores have been ongoing during the 19th and 20th centuries. In the 1950's, fill and soil were used to extend the head of the island for the purpose of creating another parking lot.

   Also in the 1950's, fill and soil were placed on the part of the Horseshoe Falls previously known as Terrapin Rocks. Terrapin "Point" is now a popular viewing area.

   Goat Island is best visited by walking to it from the mainland. Once there, continue on foot and slowly take in the wonderful scenery — the rapids, cascades, forest, wildflowers, birds, mist, rainbows, sky, other islands, and, of course, the falls.

Present Named Islands in the American Rapids

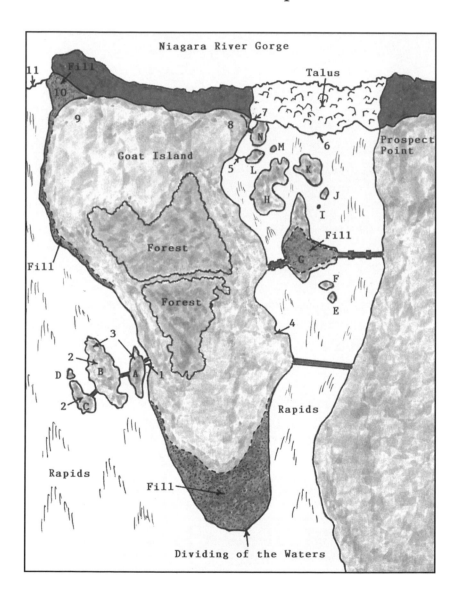

Present Named Islands in the American Rapids

I. The Three Sisters Islands
- A. Asenath
- B. Angeline
- C. Celinda Eliza

II. Other islands
- D. Solon (Little Brother Island)
- E. Brig Island
- F. Ship Island
- G. Green Island
- H. Bird Island
- I. Avery's Rock
- J. Chapin Island
- K. Robinson Island
- L. Crow Island
- M. Seldom Seen Island
- N. Luna Island

III. Points of interest
1. The Hermit's Cascade
2. Ancient rapids
3. Glacial erratics
4. Spring
5. Olmsted Cascade
6. American Falls
7. Bridal Veil Falls
8. Stedman's Bluff
9. Porter's Bluff
10. Terrapin Point
11. Horseshoe Falls

2. **Green Island.** This island of about 2 acres (8,094 square meters) between the mainland and Goat Island was covered with maple, poplar and cedar trees until 1826, when it became the location of a paper mill. From then until 1885, it had been transformed into an industrial and commercial center.

In 1885 the island became part of the state natural reserve. All structures were removed, and a more natural setting was created. In 1900 fill was placed on most of the island to make it level with the new stone bridges.

Green Island is a perfect place to relax, to get "away from it all." The sound of the rapids is quite soothing. The scenery is inspiring.

3. **Ship and Brig Islands.** Lying in the rapids just above Green Island, they have often reminded people of sailing ships, especially in the winter, when the tree trunks resemble masts. With less water in the rapids now, a number of smaller islands have formed around Ship and Brig Islands.

Prevailing winds from the south and west drive ice floes from Lake Erie into the American Rapids in the winter. The ice collects around all the islands. Since the depth of the rapids around Ship and Brig Islands has never been as great as elsewhere, ice often blocks the water from passing by. In the past, when the amount of ice coming from the lake was not controlled, the rest of the American Rapids would sometimes freeze up completely, turning off the Bridal Veil and American Falls.

4. **Avery's Rock.** Named after a man who clung to it for awhile after a boating accident in the 19th century, this rock is like so many in the rapids which lie on the bedrock.

5. **Chapin Island.** This is one of many islets in the rapids. Despite the lack of an appreciable amount of soil, plants thrive here.

6. **Robinson Island.** Like the other islands close to the falls, the trees and shrubs here are at the mercy of frozen mist in the

winter. In the spring and summer, birds nest here, protected from all but aerial predators.

7. **Bird Island.** This island and its surrounding waters are frequented by many kinds of birds, including ducks and gulls.

8. **Crow Island.** Resting next to the Olmsted Cascade, this island is also a popular resting and nesting place for birds.

9. **Seldom Seen Island.** Now larger than before, this islet is now always seen, except when covered with ice.

10. **Luna Island.** In 1905, Alfred Russel Wallace described his visit to Luna Island as

> *"A lovely sight; the arbor-vitae trees (Thuya Americana), with which it is covered, young and old, some torn and jagged, but all to the smallest twigs coated with glistening ice [his visit was in winter] from the frozen spray, looked like groves of gigantic tree corals — the most magnificent and fairy-like scene I have ever beheld. I was never tired of the ever-changing aspects of this grand illustration of natural forces engaged in modelling the earth's surface."*

Before there were bridges to it, people went to Luna Island using trees bent over the rapids. That must have been a memorable experience. Then wooden bridges were used, but they usually had to be replaced every spring, because of ice damage. Today, this island between the Bridal Veil and American Falls is visited via a solid concrete and steel bridge.

Luna Island is so named because of the lunar bows once commonly seen from there on nights with a full moon. The faint bows, some of them complete circles, must have inspired many marriage proposals and loving embraces.

The island is made up of about three-fourths of an acre (3,035 square meters) of very hard dolostone covered with a

thin layer of sandy soil. Once growing here was a thick grove
of cedar trees with tall, wide, whitish trunks. Their extended
boughs left little room for the shrubs that grew between them.
Many eagles and cedar waxwings nested in this ideal setting.

Luna Island was closed in 1954 and 1955 so that remedial
work could be accomplished. Loose rock was removed and the
dolostone ledge above the Cave of the Winds was blasted away.
The island was closed again from 1969 to 1973, once again because of dangerous conditions and the need for remedial work.

Luna Island is probably the best place to experience the
falls closeup. It is also a great place to view the Upper Great
Gorge. Gulls soar all around, sometimes in a frenzy, while the
mist is at the mercy of sudden updrafts and gusts of wind.

11. **The Three Sisters Islands, and Little Brother Island.** Geolo-
gists say that all of the islands south of Goat Island were once
part of the island, but erosion wore away all but the most resistant parts. Evidence that the islands were once submerged beneath the rapids is quite obvious, from the smooth surfaces of
the rocks to pot holes. Today, the four islands are surrounded
by wonderfully picturesque cascades and rapids, well worth
seeing and hearing.

(A) **Asenath** (The First Sister Island). Ducks spend a lot of time
in the relatively quiet waters around this island. In the
spring and summer, the red-winged blackbirds sing and
try to chase everyone away.

On the west side of Asenath is a large glacial erratic, a
boulder of gneiss, a metamorphic rock brought down hundreds of miles from Canada by a glacier during the Ice Age.

Connecting Goat Island to Asenath is the Hermit's
Cascade, named after a young man who spent two years
living by the falls in the 19th century. He was supposedly
seen bathing in the cascade more than once. Louis Agassiz,
the famous naturalist, also bathed there under the light of
a full moon.

One of the glacial erratics on the Second Sister Island.

Bedrock on the Third Sister Island eroded when under the Canadian Rapids and later polished by tourists.

(B) **Angeline** (The Second Sister Island). There are at least 16 glacial erratics scattered about on the west side of this island — all are gneiss. The whole island clearly appears to have been part of the local rapids in the not too distant past, geologically speaking.

The path around Angeline is rugged, but well worth traversing. Along the way, respect for the flora is very important, since their condition is delicately balanced.

The rapids and cascades between this island and the third are breathtaking and dangerous. They and all the other rapids above the falls are remnants of an ancient preglacial valley.

(C) **Celinda Eliza** (The Third Sister Island). The following article from the *Niagara Falls Gazette* of Wednesday, February 21, 1883, describes a natural landmark which touched the lives of many people.

> *"Nearly every person who has visited the Sister Islands within the past few years, or in fact ever since the bridges were built (1869), will recall to mind the trunk of a tree which had fallen over the rapids at the head of the Third Sister Island, and although dead, was held in position by the roots being firmly imbedded in the rock. From no point on the Island could a more magnificent view of the river and rapids be obtained, than when standing on the trunk of this old tree, which projected so far over the foaming rapids. For many years it has withstood the storms of winter, and upheld the heavy loads of ice, affording a pleasant resting place in summer for the thousands of tourists. The heavy storms of the past few weeks, have however proved too much, and an unsightly stump is all that is left to mark the spot."*

Celinda Eliza has suffered much from natural and artificial erosion. It was once home to stunted cedars and pines, as well as a variety of deciduous trees. People have removed the mosses which covered the many bold rocks.

That the nearby rapids covered this island in the past is certain. The dolostone reveals the power of the current travelling at 28 miles per hour (45 kilometers per hour).

The view of the Canadian Rapids from Celinda Eliza rivals the cataracts below. Just imagine twice as much water there — or more!

(D) **Little Brother Island.** This tiny island is separated from Celinda Eliza by a narrow but dangerously swift stream.

Little Brother Island.

Chapter 3:

The Natural History of the Niagara Falls and Their Gorge

"Onward proud River! — many a voiceless century
Into the shadow past had vanished recordless,
Did not the lines and chinks of thy shrewd chiselling,
Scarring the polished tablets of thy cenotaph,
Tell us the mystic story of thy genesis."

James Warner Ward, 1886

"If New York has a single natural symbol that is almost in-
stantly recognizable to much of the rest of the world, it is
Niagara Falls. Niagara Falls are dynamic geology, geology
that can be timed on the human clock, geology we can see hap-
pening. The account of the formation of the falls and gorge is
one of the most fascinating geologic stories ever written."

Bradford B. Van Diver, 1985

Before the Ice Age

All of the bedrock in the Niagara Region is sedimentary, which
means the rock was made from sand, silt, and other deposits which
were cemented together at the bottom of ancient seas. Those deposits came from a chain of mountains which once went north to south
along the east coast of North America. Weathering slowly eroded
away even the highest peaks.

North of the Niagara Escarpment, the bedrock is composed
of late Ordovician shale which was made between 500 to 435 million years ago. From the Niagara Escarpment to the Onondaga
Escarpment, the bedrock is composed of Silurian dolostones, shales,
sandstones, and limestones, all of which were made between 435
to 395 million years ago. South of the Onondaga Escarpment, the
bedrock is composed of Devonian limestones, shales, and sandstones which were made between 395 to 345 million years ago.

The Ordovician bedrock from the Niagara Escarpment to Lake
Ontario is known as Queenston shale. About 1,200 feet (3,658
meters) thick, this red rock was deposited along a coastal plain
which stretched from New York to Virginia. The iron-rich muds
and silts were exposed to the oxygen in the atmosphere, hence the
red color (iron oxide, or rust).

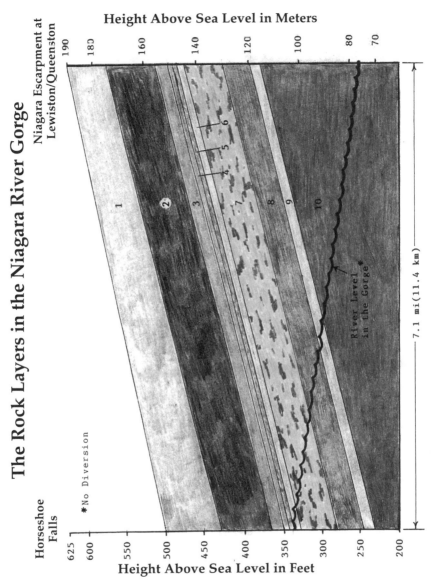

The Rock Layers in the Niagara River Gorge

Height Above Sea Level in Meters

Height Above Sea Level in Feet

Niagara Escarpment at Lewiston/Queenston

Horseshoe Falls

*No Diversion

River Level in the Gorge*

7.1 mi(11.4 km)

1. Lockport Dolostone
2. Rochester Shale
3. Irondequoit Limestone
4. Reynales Limestone
5. Neahga Shale

6. Thorold Sandstone
7. Grimsby Sandstone
8. Power Glen Shale
9. Whirlpool Sandstone
10. Queenston Shale

The Queenston shale does not contain fossils because life forms had not yet adapted to the environment in which it formed. The best place to see the shale is at the mouth of the Niagara River Gorge, at either Queenston, Ontario, or Lewiston, New York.

There are a number of layers of different Silurian rocks in the Niagara Gorge, and, in recent years, they have been divided into many sublayers. For general interest, only the 10 major layers will be discussed.

1. **Whirlpool Sandstone.** From 15 to 25 feet (4.6 to 7.6 meters) thick, it is light gray to white in color. Where it is exposed, it often exhibits ripple and wave marks. It contains what are probably the oldest Silurian fossils in North America — ostracodes, trilobites, and lingulid brachiopods.

   Whirlpool Sandstone was formed in a shallow sea. This explains the ripple and wave marks. The best place to see it is at the Whirlpool in the Niagara Gorge, especially when the water is low.

2. **Power Glen Shale.** From 34 to 36 feet (10.1 to 11 meters) thick, it is gray to greenish-gray in color. It also exhibits a few ripple marks. It does not contain many good fossils. They are usually fragmented.

   Power Glen Shale was formed along the shoreline of an ancient sea which was moving eastward. Tidal currents deposited some thin layers of sand in the shale.

3. **Grimsby Sandstone.** From 42 to 52 feet (12.8 to 15.8 meters) thick, this rock is easily identified by its mottled appearance, spots or blotches of pale green or yellow surrounded by red. The lowest part of the Grimsby Sandstone was formed in a shallow delta which produced some fossils of brachiopods and pelecypods. The middle part was formed from mudflats, while the top part was made when the sea returned to the site, leaving behind worm burrows and fossils of lingulid brachiopods.

   During the formation of the Grimsby Sandstone, the sea affecting it moved west, and then east.

4. **Thorold Sandstone.** This layer is from 4.6 to 9.7 feet (1.4 to 3 meters) thick. It is white to buff in color. Like the other rock layers in the gorge, this one only has fossils of simple animals, animals without backbones (invertebrates), such as brachiopods.

   Thorold Sandstone was made from Grimsby Sandstone which was eroded along the beach of an ancient sea.

5. **Neahga Shale.** From 6 to 7 feet (1.8 to 2.1 meters) in thickness, this layer has very small amounts of limestone mixed with the green and olive-green shales. It contains very few fossils.

   Neahga Shale formed in a very shallow and stagnant sea.

6. **Reynales Limestone.** From 11.5 to 15.25 feet (3.5 to 4.7 meters) thick, this layer is dark gray to gray blue in color. It contains pyrite (iron sulfide or "fool's gold"). It also contains fossils of at least 81 species of invertebrates.

   Reynales Limestone, a very hard and durable rock was formed when the shore of an ancient sea was drying up.

7. **Irondequoit Limestone.** It varies from 6 to 9.5 feet (1.8 to 2.9 meters) in thickness, and it changes from a light or dark gray to white and tan when weathered. It contains at least 69 species of invertebrate fossils, including brachiopods, crinoids, bryozoans, and corals. Most of the fossils are concentrated in the upper foot (0.3 meter) of this layer.

   Irondequoit Limestone formed in a shallow sea.

8. **Rochester Shale.** Its thickness ranges from 55 to 65 feet (16.8 to 19.8 meters). The lower half of this layer is dark brownish gray, while the upper half is dark bluish gray. The whole layer has more varieties of fossils than any other Silurian formation in the world. There are well-preserved crinoids, bryozoans, brachiopods, cephalopods, and trilobites.

   Rochester Shale was formed at the bottom of a somewhat deeper sea than those which formed the other Silurian layers in the gorge.

9. **Lockport Dolostone.** From the Niagara Escarpment to the Horseshoe Falls, the thickness of the Lockport Dolostone increases from about 50 feet (15 meters) to 65 feet (20 meters); then it increases another 55 feet (17 meters) from the Horseshoe Falls to the upper end or head of the Canadian Rapids. Like the other layers of bedrock in the gorge, the Lockport Dolostone layer is tilted to the south about 20 feet (6 meters) per mile. It comes in a variety of colors: dark gray, blue, pink, brownish-gray, olive-gray, and grayish-brown.

Lockport Dolostone formed at the bottom of shallow warm seas. Unlike limestone, which is made of calcium carbonate, dolostone is made from calcium magnesium carbonate, making it harder than limestone, but somewhat brittle. There are different sublayers of dolostone in the Niagara Gorge, each distinct in its chemical composition (impurities) and method of deposition. They are, from the oldest to newest:

(A) **Decew Dolostone.** Ranging from 5.6 to 12 feet (1.7 to 3.7 meters) in thickness, this very finely crystalline dolostone is medium to dark gray in color. It contains some fossils — many burrows.

(B) **Gasport Dolostone.** From 15 to 44.5 feet (4.6 to 13.6 meters) thick, it is more like limestone than dolostone. Its color is blue to gray, with some pink scattered about. It contains limestone and reef structures. Fossils are abundant, especially crinoids.

(C) **Goat Island Dolostone.** This layer ranges from 17.5 to 26 feet (5.3 to 7.9 meters) in thickness, and its color is mostly light olive-gray to brownish-gray. What fossils there are are usually poorly preserved — brachiopods, stromatoporoids, and corals are most common.

(D) **Eramosa Dolostone.** From 13.5 to 15 feet (4.1 to 4.6 meters) thick, this layer is medium gray to grayish-brown in color.

The American side of the Lewiston Branch Gorge.

Lockport Dolostone at Prospect Point.

The Whirlpool Rapids and the Whirlpool Rapids Gorge.

The Lower Great Gorge, Part 1, the Devil's Hole Rapids, and the lower part of the Niagara Glen.

The Old Narrow Gorge, with the Canadian hydroelectric plants on the right and the American plant on the left.

Hubbard Point, just right of center, in the Upper Great Gorge.

The American Rapids.

The Canadian Rapids.

The American and Bridal Veil Falls.

Talus below the American and Bridal Veil Falls.

Gulls soaring in the mist above the Horseshoe Falls.

Terrapin Point in the foreground; the Horseshoe Falls in the background.

Frozen mist on the trees above the American Falls.

A typical ice bridge in the Upper Great Gorge.

Historical houses at the top of the ancient shore of Niagara Island.

Olmsted Cascade, in the rapids above the Bridal Veil Falls,
was named after Frederick Law Omsted, the man who designed
Niagara Reservation State Park.

It also contains chert. Fossils in it are not common. There are some brachiopods, corals, gastropods, and bryozoans.

(E) **Oak Orchard Dolostone.** The bottom 1.5 to 4 feet (0.5 to 1.2 meters) of this layer form the caprock of the American and Bridal Veil Falls. The beds of the American and Canadian Rapids are also made of this layer. Oak Orchard Dolostone reaches its maximum thickness of about 120 feet (36.5 meters) south of the Niagara Falls. If the Horseshoe Falls were permitted to recede naturally, it would someday get to a point by Grand Island where its waters would be falling from Oak Orchard Dolostone into a pool with a bed made of the same rock. This would stop the falls, for all intents and purposes, from continuing to erode its way south.

Fossils are scarce. There are some corals, stromatolites (algae), stromatoporoids (primitive sponges), brachiopods (primitive clamlike animals), and ostracodes (primitive crustaceans).

The Ice Age

Known to scientists as the Pleistocene Epoch, the last Ice Age began about one million years ago and ended about 10,000 years ago. It appears that there were four advances from and retreats to the north. The last advance is called the Wisconsin Stage.

The time between advances are known as inter-glacial periods, and they lasted about 12,500 years. The weather warmed up during these periods, just like now. It has been about 12,500 years since the glaciers last left this part of North America. Does that mean that another advance is imminent?

Wisconsin glaciation took place in three parts: Early Wisconsin, which began between 150,000 to 180,000 years ago; Middle Wisconsin, which began about 42,000 years ago; the Late Wisconsin, which began about 23,000 years ago. The last glacier buried the St. David's Falls, its gorge, and the river which created them.

Each time a glacier came down from Canada, its enormous weight pushed Earth's crust into its elastic mantle, the amount depending on the thickness of the ice. The last glacier pushed the crust in the Niagara Region down about 175 feet (53 meters). Is the crust still rising or rebounding? Yes.

The glaciers transformed vast rivers and their valleys into the basins for the present Great Lakes and Finger Lakes. When the last glacier began to melt and retreat, a large lake, Lake Lundy, formed in and around the Niagara Region. As the crust kept rising, the Niagara Escarpment emerged from the water, creating two separate lakes which would later become Lakes Erie and Ontario.

The precursor of Lake Erie flooded much of the Tonawanda and Huron Plains, forming shallow Lakes Tonawanda and Wainfleet. The amount of flooding on the plains was affected by the changes in the amount of water coming from Lake Erie.

For only one or two hundred years, Lake Tonawanda sent water over the Niagara Escarpment in five places. One by one, the spillways to the east of the Niagara River dried up as Earth's crust kept rising. About 12,000 years ago, only the Niagara River emptied into the precursor ("Lake Iroquois") of Lake Ontario.

After the Ice Age

The tectonic forces which raised the layers of rock in the Niagara Region at an angle fractured the rock in many places, creating joints and faults. A joint is a fracture in a rock along which displacement or movement has not occurred. A fault is a joint along which movement has occurred.

Ground water gets into the joints and faults, moving horizontally, vertically, and diagonally. Whenever ground water comes out as a spring, weathering of the rock, especially due to freezing and thawing of the water, causes rockfalls and rockslides.

Along the Niagara Escarpment, rocks which fall accumulate at the bottom, forming a pile called "talus." Further weathering eventually erodes the talus into particles of sand and silt.

When the water from Lake Tonawanda began pouring over the Niagara Escarpment at Lewiston/Queenston, it had enough power to speed up the erosion of the talus, by grinding stones and rocks into each other. Also, the masses of ice which formed below the falls helped to crack up the rocks.

Since the hardest rock in the Niagara Region is the Lockport Dolostone, it was last to fall to the bottom of the falls. This simple fact has made it possible for the falls to recede and create the gorge. Whenever there was a lot of water going over the falls and/or when the crestline of the falls was jagged and unstable, the falls receded more quickly than when there was less water going over and/or the crestline had the more stable horseshoe-like shape.

If the falls had the horseshoe shape and a lot of water going over it, it still didn't move back quickly, but it had plenty of time to erode the talus and create a deep plunge pool. Such is the case at today's Horseshoe Falls.

There is not complete agreement among scientists on exactly how and when the Niagara River Gorge formed. Presented here is a general history of gorge formation. It is divided into six parts.

Part 1. Formation of the Lewiston Branch Gorge. This gorge formed from about 12,300 to 12,000 years ago, in only 300 years. It is about 2,001 feet (610 meters) long and 1,401 feet (427 meters) wide.

The waterfall dropped from the Lockport Dolostone into Lake Iroquois, a distance of about 50 to 60 feet (15 to 18 meters), eroding the Rochester Shale to the Irondequoit Limestone. Its rate of recession was about 6.66 feet (2.03 meters) a year.

The amount of water in the falls was probably about the same as the amount of water which comes from Lake Erie today, a little over 200,000 cubic feet (5,663 cubic meters) per second.

The Whirlpool in the foreground; the buried St. David's Gorge in the background.

The Lewiston Branch Gorge in the foreground, the Lower Niagara River in the background.

The Lewiston Branch Gorge is easily seen and visited from Lewiston, New York, at Artpark, and from Queenston, Ontario. On both sides of the river, there are trails into the gorge. The views are breathtaking, especially of the gorge walls and the lower river.

Part 2. Formation of the Old Narrow Gorge. This gorge was made between 12,000 and 11,000 years ago. It is about 6.365 feet (1,940 meters) long and 1,299 feet (396 meters) wide.

The falls was still not very high, perhaps 60 to 80 feet (18 to 24 meters). Some scientists say the amount of water coming through the river at this time was small, perhaps 15% of the flow today, while others say the flow was much like today's. Whatever the case, the falls receded at an appreciable rate of about 6.36 feet (1.94 meters) a year.

For awhile, at the site of the Smeaton Ravine (near the floral clock) there was one large falls and a smaller one separated by an island somewhat like today's American and Bridal Veil Falls. The best time to see the Smeaton Ravine and its dry falls is in the autumn from the American side of the gorge.

Part 3. The Lower Great Gorge, Part 1. From the Old Narrow Gorge to the lower end of the Niagara Glen, this gorge is about 3,117 feet (950 meters) long and 1,148 to 1,601 feet (350 to 488 meters) wide. It was formed between about 11,500 to 10,500 years ago, in about 500 years. The amount of water going over the falls was about the same as the present flow from Lake Erie, and the rate of recession of the falls was about 6.23 feet (1.90 meters) a year.

During the formation of this gorge, Lake Iroquois dropped more than 90 feet (27 meters), resulting in the appearance of a second falls at Lewiston/Queenston where water poured off the Irondequoit Limestone into a pool which had the Whirlpool Sandstone for its bed. This lower falls soon caught up with the upper falls, making one falls with a height of about 150 to 160 feet (46 to 49 meters). Where is it thought the two falls caught up with each other? Near Devil's Hole State Park and the lower end of the Niagara Glen.

After the higher falls passed the other outlet from Lake Tonawanda into the Niagara River at the site of today's Devil's Hole State Park, a small falls started flowing there, creating the ravine seen today. That small falls eventually diminished to a small stream.

Obviously, the best places to see this gorge are from the Niagara Glen and Devil's Hole State Park. It is also possible to venture into the gorge in both places.

Part 4. The Lower Great Gorge, Part 2, or Nippising Lower Great Gorge. Starting from the lower end of the Niagara Glen, and ending at the Whirlpool, this gorge formed between about 10,500 to 4,200 years ago, nearly 6,300 years. It is about 4,291 feet (1,308 meters) long and 1,148 feet (350 meters) wide. Here the falls receded very slowly, about 0.79 of a foot (0.24 of a meter) a year.

Why did the falls move so slowly? Because the amount of water coming from Lake Erie dropped to about 15% of its present amount.

Lake Iroquois dropped again, becoming salty after mixing with water from the Atlantic Ocean. Then another lower falls formed at Lewiston/Queenston, where water poured from the Whirlpool Sandstone into a pool with a bed made of the soft Queenston Shale. This falls quickly caught up with the falls at the upper end of the Niagara Glen, forming a falls about 150 to 160 feet (46 to 49 meters) high.

At the Niagara Glen, there was an island with two falls on each side, one small, the other much larger. The larger falls passed the island and captured the water going over the smaller falls. The island later collapsed, forming the beautiful glen. The remains of the small dry falls and the bed of the upper river above it can be visited and easily identified.

The best places to see this gorge are the Niagara Glen and Whirlpool State Park, from the top or bottom.

Part 5. The Whirlpool and the Whirlpool Rapids Gorge. During the last interglacial period, another river cut out a gorge from the Niagara Escarpment. When the last Wisconsin glacier arrived, it buried the gorge and its cataract. This gorge is named after the small community located on the site of its mouth, St. David's, Ontario.

After the glacier melted away, the present Niagara River followed part of the path of the earlier stream, including the upper part of the buried gorge. When the Lewiston/Queenston falls reached the St. David's Gorge, solid rock suddenly gave way to all kinds of debris, such as sand, silt, and the remains of plants and animals. What a muddy stream the river must have been. When did this all happen? In just 200 years, between 4,200 and 4,000 years ago.

Thus was formed the fabulous and eery Whirlpool, a sharp right turn in the Niagara River. The rest of the upper end of the St. David's Gorge was also cleaned out, allowing the buried falls to be reborn, about 4,000 years ago. What a sight that must have been!

The naturally exhumed gorge is known as the Whirlpool Rapids Gorge. It is about 7,792 feet (2,375 meters) long and about 755 to 1,968 feet (230 to 600 meters) wide. The amount of water coming into the Niagara River from Lake Erie at the time of the exhumation is debatable, from 15% to 100% of today's flow.

The best places to view the Whirlpool and Whirlpool Rapids Gorge are Whirlpool State Park (its upper and lower trails, the Whirlpool Rapids Bridge (walking), and all the parkland on the Canadian side, including the scenic natural trail at the Whirlpool.

Part 6. The Upper Great Gorge. After the St. David's Falls was reborn, the amount of water coming from Lake Erie remained fairly steadily at the present flow. This made it possible for the single falls to erode a wide (1,600 feet or 489 meters) gorge with deep plunge pools.

For the past 4,000 years, the falls, today's Horseshoe Falls, receded at a rate of 3 to 6 feet (.9 to 1.8 meters) a year. Its Gorge is about 10,560 feet (3,219 meters) long.

When the falls reached an elevation in the bedrock called Hubbard Point, it began to decrease in height as it descended an ancient valley. Today, the Horseshoe Falls is at the bottom of that valley, having lost about 55 feet (17 meters).

The American and Bridal Veil Falls were made about 900 to 700 years ago, as the Horseshoe Falls went by Goat Island. What a sight it must have been when they were still attached — one monstrous cataract.

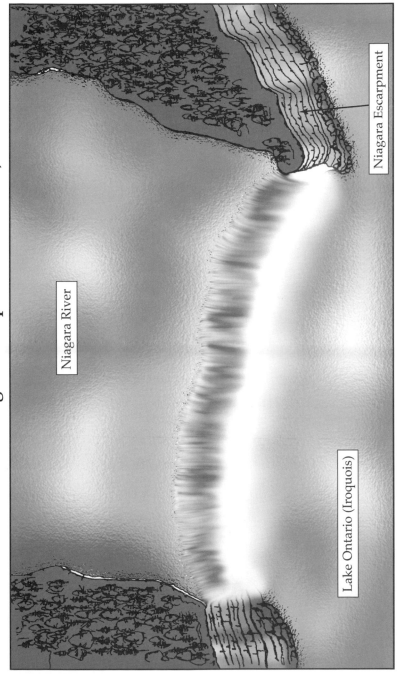

The Falls at the Niagara Escarpment Around 12,300 BP

Niagara Escarpment

Niagara River

Lake Ontario (Iroquois)

The Falls at the Niagara Glen and Devil's Hole Around 10,000 BP

Niagara River

Niagara Island

Lake Tonawanda

Small Falls (now dry) at future site of Niagara Glen

Small island (now collapsed) at future site of Niagara Glen

Future site of the Devil's Hole

Dry Riverbed

No Falls at the Buried St. David's Gorge from Around 4,200 to 4,000 BP

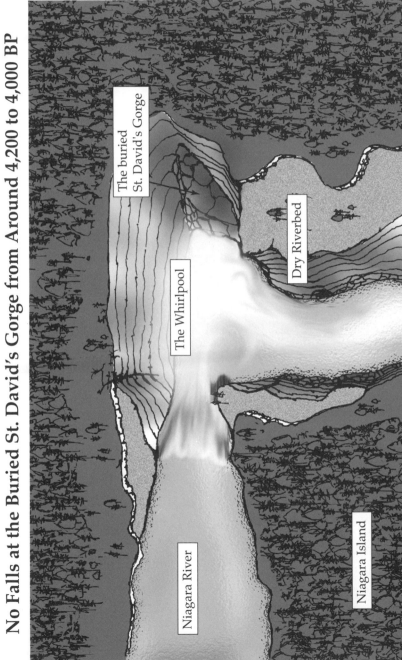

The buried St. David's Gorge

Dry Riverbed

The Whirlpool

Niagara River

Niagara Island

The Rebirth of the St. David's Falls (Now the Horseshoe Falls) Around 4,000 BP

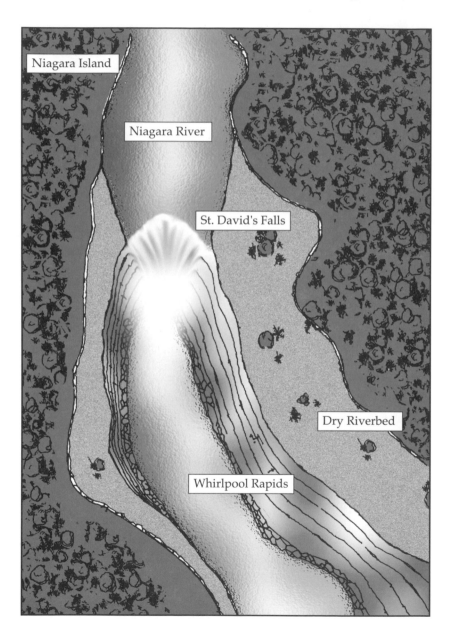

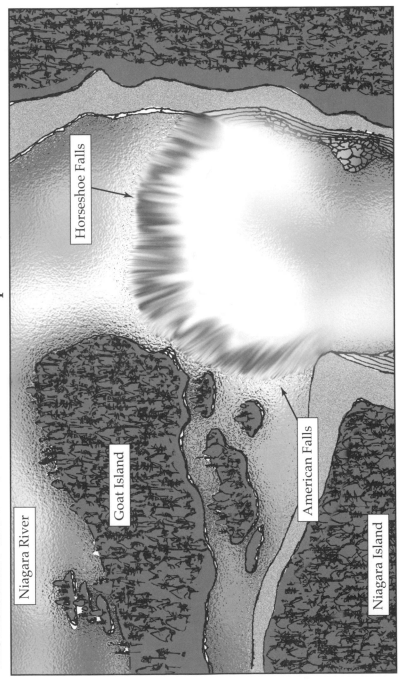

The Horseshoe and American Falls About to separate at Goat Island around 700 BP

Horseshoe Falls

American Falls

Niagara River

Goat Island

Niagara Island

Chapter 4:

Niagara's Wild Animals and Plants

Wild Animals

"The celebrated Cataract of Niagara is a noted place of resort for the bald eagle, as well on account of the fish procured there, as for the numerous carcasses of squirrels, deer, bears, and various other animals, that, in their attempts to cross the river above the Falls, have been dragged into the current, and precipitated down that tremendous gulf, where, among the rocks that bound the Rapids below, they furnish a rich repast for the vulture, the raven, and the bald eagle."

Alexander Wilson and Charles L. Bonaparte, 1831

Even though human activities have seriously affected the populations of many of the wild animals in the Niagara Region, there are still a great number of species residing there.

Niagara's Amphibians and Reptiles

"Residents on the other side of the river (Canada) have been much interested during the past week in a large rattlesnake which was captured at Foster's flats (down in the Niagara Glen), a place which in past years was the home of countless rattlers. There was a time when the rattlers were numerous in that vicinity, but at the present time they are seen occasionally, although it is stated that a person on a snake hunt would have no trouble in scaring one up if he so desired."

Niagara Falls Gazette, July 11, 1902

The amphibians and reptiles living in the Niagara Region are usually not easy to see because of their cryptic habits and appearances. Some, such as the Copperhead Snake and Timber Rattlesnake, once quite common, have not been seen for many years. Those known to still inhabit the region include 10 species of frog (Bull-, Chorus, Common Tree, Green, Leopard, Pickerel, Spotted, Spring Peeper, Striped, and Wood); the Mudpuppy or Waterdog; two species of newts (Eastern and red-spotted); 3 species of salamander (Blue-spotted, Jefferson, and Red-back; the Five-lined Skink; 14 species of snakes (Black Racer, Common Rat, Fox, Garter, Hog-nosed, King, Little Brown, Massasauga Rattle-, Milk, Redbelly, Ribbon, Ring-necked, Smooth Green, and Water); the American Toad; 10 species of turtles (Blanding's, Box, Common Snapper, Map, Musk, Painted, Soft-shelled, Spotted, Stinkpot, and wood).

Niagara's Fish

"A Gentleman who was Travelling this Part, went to see this Heap, which comes from a River in the North, and Falls into a great Basin of Lake Outano (Ontario), big enough to hold a Hundred Men of War, being there he taught the Natives to catch Fish with their Hands, by causing Trees to be cut down in the Spring, and to be rolled to the Bank of the River, so that he might be upon them without wetting himself; by the Assistance of which he thrust his Arm into the Water up to the Elbow, where he found a prodigious Quantity of Fish of different Species, which he laid hold on by the Gills, gently stroking 'em, and when he had taken Fifty or Sixty of 'em at a Time, he use to warm and refresh himself; after this Manner, in a short Time he would catch Fish enough to feed Fifty or Sixty families."

Four Native American Princes, 1710

The Niagara River has more kinds of fish than any other river in North America. The diversity is a result of the local climate, geography and geological history.

Among those living in the river are: Alewife, White Bass, White Perch Bass, Carp, Brown and Channel Catfish, Yellow Bullhead, Catfish, Burbot Cod, Sheepshead or Freshwater Drum, American Eel, Long Nose Gar, Goldfish, Sea Lamprey, Silver Lamprey, many species of Minnow, Muskellunge, many species of Perch, Northern Pike, Chinook and Coho Salmon, Lake Sturgeon, and Rainbow Trout.

Niagara's Birds

"It is said that birds which fly over the fall are drawn into it in spite of themselves, by the force of the air. I am not sure of this fact, which, however, is not lacking in probability, since there is often seen there a rainbow which seems strongly to attract the birds who direct their flight into it, where they become confused and drenched, lacking strength to ascend. And it may perhaps be only birds of passage, for those which inhabit the neighborhood are so accustomed to the rainbow and to the noise from the fall that they know how to preserve themselves, since they are seldom seen there, although there are a great many of them in this vicinity."

M. Bonnefons, 1753

There were once many more birds by the Niagara River and its falls. Those left are always a delight to behold. One of them, the Bluebird Thrush or Eastern Bluebird, the official New York State bird, is rare, but making a comeback.

In 1996, the Canadian Nature Federation, Bird Studies Canada, National Audubon Society, Partners in Flight, and the American Bird Conservatory officially designated the Niagara River area as an Important Bird Area — part of a world-wide effort to identify and preserve habitats critical to birds.

There are about 235 different species of birds which either visit or live in the Niagara Region.

Ring-billed Gulls resting in the calm waters between Goat Island and the First Sister Island.

A Gray Squirrel having a snack on Goat Island.

Niagara's Mammals

"Of the fauna of Niagara very much cannot be said. All the larger Mammalia, which abounded in the region whilst it was still the possession of the red man, have long since disappeared. It seems almost as though they could never have resorted, habitually, to Goat Island. The access to it of the elk, the red deer, the bear, the panther, the lynx, the fox, and the wolf, common enough in the neighborhood, must always have been difficult, and their return to the mainland almost impossible. At the present time the quadrupeds inhabiting the island are probably only three, the Black-squirrel, the Red-squirrel, and the Striped-squirrel or Chipmunk. These may be seen, almost any spring or summer day, disporting themselves, without regard to the presence of man, in their leafy coverts."

David F. Day, 1901

Gone, probably forever, from Western New York and the Niagara Peninsula are wild wolves, moose, mountain lions, caribou and lynx. They were either killed off by or could not compete with the ever increasing human populations of the past two or three centuries.

There are still, however, many kinds of mammals in the Niagara region, and some, such as the white-tailed deer and gray squirrel have actually benefited from human activities.

Wild Plants

"As one of the scenic wonders of the world, Niagara Falls and the Great Gorge fascinate not only the casual sight-seer but the earnest student of nature as well. While the scene encountered owes its grandeur primarily to geological features — the roaring cataract, and the deep canyon and precipitous cliffs north of the Falls — the vegetation that presents itself lends

tone and color to the rugged landscape. Though appearing in masses only in restricted areas, the flora (plants) is withal rich and varied, Day's Catalogue of the Niagara Flora (1887) enumerating as many as 909 species of flowering and fern-like plants growing without cultivation in the vicinity of Niagara Falls."

Charles A. Zenkert, 1934

"To the Victorian naturalists a hundred years ago, the attraction and wonder of Goat Island and the Niagara River Gorge was less the superb view of the Falls than the plants underfoot and overhead."

Lisa Aug, 1987

The Niagara Region, especially around the Niagara Gorge and Falls, has had a great variety of plants thriving in the temperate climate. In most places the sometimes unique verdant landscape had yielded to settlement, industry and development. Try to imagine the original setting. Let the imagination create the Edenic scene in all its breathtaking glory.

Fungi and Lichens

"Knowledge of plants is critical to understanding how the world works. Plants constitute 99.9 percent of the Earth's biomass, while animals account for only 0.1 percent. This means that plants are basically all that's on the planet."

Doug Larson, 1994

Fungi and lichens help nature recycle things, from dead trees to rocks. Forests of long ago have been turned into forests of today. Rocks of long ago have been turned into soil. The environment in the Niagara Region, especially around the falls, allows fungi and lichens to thrive.

Niagara's Mosses

"Smaller than either of the others, yet grander in its scenery is the third Sister Island. A little channel of swiftly running water divides it at the foot so that in reality there are four sisters instead of three. Here the grandeur, beauty and wildness of the others combined breaks upon the vision. All around roaring waters — huge boulders of moss-covered rocks — stunted trees and thick shrubbery, deep crevices in the rocks, over which one may leap if he will, but must do so with firm nerves and well judging eye."

Niagara Falls Gazette, July 12, 1871

The Three Sisters Islands were once known as the Moss Islands. In those days, before great amounts of water were diverted upriver for the hydroelectric power plants, the atmosphere around the islands was more moist, allowing mosses to flourish on the rocks and soil.

Ferns and Fern Allies

"It has been said that the area including the Niagara Peninsula and the Southern Frontier of New York State was the fern capital of the world during the Victorian era when extensive collections of exotica were in vogue."

K. D. Eaton, 1991

While strolling over the beautiful old stone bridge to the First Sister Island, early on a summer morning, look for tiny delicate ferns growing on its surface. Also look for ferns in the gorge, especially where conditions are shady and moist.

Niagara's Wonderful Wildflowers

"The species richness in this area is wonderful. There are over 900 varieties of plants to be found in this area alone. This is a diversity one would expect on a regional, not a local scale. It's obviously an unusual biological situation. That's the beauty of it. This is a very exciting, very dynamic environment, and the vegetation types reflect that."

Patricia Eckel, 1987

Many of the wildflowers in the Niagara Region are now rare. It is therefore extremely important that they be left alone. Not even their blossoms should be removed, as that would negatively affect pollination and reproduction. All of the wildflowers should be unaffected by human behavior, unless it is absolutely necessary to do so. Niagara's floral treasure must be around for future generations of people to observe and enjoy.

There are about 909 different kinds of wildflowers native to the Niagara Region. Many of them are rare or endangered.

Niagara's Trees and Shrubs

"It would be difficult to find within another territory so restricted in its limits so great a diversity of trees and shrubs and still more difficult to find in so small an area such examples of arboreal symmetry and perfection as the island (Goat Island) has to exhibit. There are to be found in Western New York (and the Niagara Peninsula) about one hundred and seventy species of trees and shrubs. Goat Island and the immediate vicinity of the river near the Falls can show of these no less than one hundred and forty."

David F. Day, 1901

There are trees growing in the Niagara River Gorge which normally grow in lower latitudes in the United States. Why are they able to succeed in the gorge? The gorge offers protection from the weather and provides moisture with its many springs.

Chapter 5:

Notable Natural Phenomena

"A strange and rare sight was seen yesterday afternoon about three o'clock by a number of persons in this village, it being no less than a beautiful mirage of Niagara Falls in the clouds just above the horizon. The reflection seemed to lie directly on a bank of fleecy clouds, and was almost perfect in its detail. The Suspension Bridge could be plainly seen as well as the Falls, Goat Island and some of the surrounding buildings. The wonderful spectacle, which appeared similar to a photograph or glass of an immense scale, lasted nearly if not quite half an hour, finally dissolving slowly until it had entirely disappeared."

Tonawanda News, May 10, 1881

The Niagara Region and its world-famous cataracts have long been the scene of many natural phenomena, from immense bridges made of ice to small cedar trees thousands of years old. Read on, and learn why Niagara is not one, but *many* wonders.

Ice Bridges. Nearly every winter ice floes from Lake Erie go over Niagara Falls and mass together in the gorge from shore to shore, forming a bridge of ice over the liquid water.

On March 29, 1848, gusts of wind dammed up the Niagara River at its source, nearly drying up the falls for a day. People on both sides of the river were astounded and humbled. It was possible to frolic on the riverbed where no person had ever been.

After the dam broke up, the ice formed a bridge from just below the falls to Lake Ontario. It was possible for people go to from Niagara-on-the-Lake to Youngstown by walking or riding a horse. Ice boulders as high as 50 feet (15 meters) did a lot damage to structures along the shores of the lower Niagara River.

Until a fatal accident in 1912, people were permitted to go on the ice bridges. In January of 1938, the ice in the gorge was able to knock down the Honeymoon Bridge.

This is a depiction of Niagara Falls on March 29, 1848, the day nature almost turned them off. Only a small stream went over the center of the Horseshoe Falls. The American Falls was reduced to a few very minor falls.

The ice bridges have been less impressive since the 1960s, when Ontario Hydro and the New York Power Authority began installing the ice boom at the source of the Niagara River. The boom is a chain of floating barrels across much of the river which controls the movement of ice floes from Lake Erie.

For those who think the weather has been strange lately, a study of past meteorological events is somewhat reassuring. For example, the winter of 1865-66 was quite cold and long in the Niagara Region. There were still masses of ice in the gorge the following summer.

Winter Ice on Lakes Erie and Ontario. The amount of ice which forms on the lakes depends on their depths and the weather. Being shallower, Lake Erie cools off faster, so it forms a layer of ice over most or all of its surface most winters. Lake Ontario is usually mostly ice-free in the winter.

Earthquakes. From 1823 to 2000, at least 41 earthquakes have been felt in the Niagara Region. Twenty-eight of the quakes were centered in the Niagara Region. Richter Scale readings have varied from 2.3 to 6.2. The region has two locations with one or more faults: the Ransomville-Niagara Falls Fault and the Clarendon-Linden Fault System.

Since 1823, the frequency of earthquakes felt in the Niagara Region has been increasing. If the trend continues, there will be about 25 earthquakes between 2001 and 2050.

Rockfalls. Rocks have been falling into the Niagara River Gorge for the past 12,000 or so years, both from the walls of the gorge and from the receding falls. It is hard to imagine that the open space inside the gorge was once filled by solid rock. Where is that rock, today? It is mostly at the bottom of Lake Ontario in the form of sand and silt.

Rocks fall from the face and brink of the falls because of the freezing and thawing of groundwater in joints and faults. Ground-

Earthquakes in the Niagara Region and Known Area Fault Lines

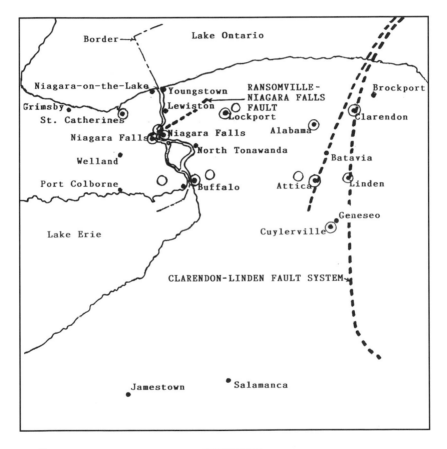

○ LOCATION OF ONE OR MORE EPICENTERS

water also makes it possible for masses of rock to slide away from the falls.

If there is enough water falling on the rocks (talus) below the falls, they are usually broken up into particles of sand and silt which are washed by strong currents in the lower Niagara River into Lake Ontario.

Weathering and the freezing and thawing of groundwater also cause rocks to fall from the walls of the gorge, especially in winter and spring.

Rainbows. On Wednesday, September 22, 1886, the *Niagara Falls Gazette* printed the following question and answer.

> *"Why should the rainbow, seen below the Niagara Falls be called by the name given to the Steamer which carries passengers around the foot of those falls? Because it is <u>made</u> of the Mist."*

Indeed, it is when the sun shines through the mist that rainbows are made. The best time to see rainbows by the falls on the American side is in the morning; the best time on the Canadian side is in the evening. Since there is now less mist by the falls than in the past, the rainbows are not as large as they could be.

The following item appeared in the *Niagara Falls Gazette* on December 5, 1891.

> *"The people of Niagara are familiar with all sizes of rainbows, for the pretty tokens are ever to be seen in the gorge, but those who missed seeing the one that hung suspended over the gorge at 7:45 o'clock Friday Morning missed a rare treat. It was a magnificent bow. It rose from the gulf a little south of Falls Street, and its line ascended very high. It was very broad and the colors were very strong and beautiful."*

Lunar Bows. Some of the sun's light is reflected off the moon's gray barren surface. Then varying amounts of that reflected light reach our planet as waxing or waning phases. When the moon is full, or reflecting light off half its surface to an observer on Earth, a very special and beautiful phenomenon can occur in the mist made by the Niagara Falls. The phenomenon is called a "moon bow" or "lunar bow."

Like a daytime rainbow, a lunar bow is made when the rays of sunlight pass through the water droplets in the mist and are then refracted. Refraction separates all the colors in the light.

A lunar bow is fainter and less colorful than its daytime cousin. A 19th-century observer said it had a

"soft, elusive character, almost ethereal, and different from the bold glaring colors seen at Niagara in the broad daylight. It usually reaches much more nearly to a full circle than that seen in daylight."

By the middle of the 20th century, the surrounding bright lights, air pollution, and great diversion of water for hydroelectric power production made it just about impossible to see a lunar bow. A bow was seen, however, on October 13, 1981, from Luna Island after the lights on the falls were turned off. It was red on the outside and yellow and blue on the inside, much like bows seen before.

The Mist above Niagara Falls. In 1801, an observer wrote,

"A cloud of vapour constantly arises from the center of the falls, part of which becomes dissolved in the higher regions of the atmosphere, and a part spreads itself in dews over the neighboring fields. This cloud of vapour has frequently, in clear weather, been observed from Lake Ontario, at the distance of 90 miles (145 kilometers) from the falls."

Whether or not Niagara's mist could be seen so far away is debatable. It is possible. Conditions long ago were not the same as today. A much greater amount of water was going over the falls, producing much more mist.

Mist rising above the great Horseshoe Falls.

Mist rising from below the American Falls.

There are three ways in which the mist forms, and the amount of mist produced in all three cases depends upon: the relative humidity and temperature of the ambient air; the difference between the air and water temperatures; the amount of water going over the falls. Cool, damp air cannot absorb as much of the mist as warm, dry air. When the air is warmer than the water it absorbs the mist more than when it colder than the water.

The three methods in which mist forms over the falls are: (A) when some of the water going over the falls evaporates, rises, cools, and then condenses in the air; (B) when air is taken below the water at the base of one of the falls, compressed, and then quickly comes up and explodes, spraying mist into the air; (C) when the falling water strikes rocks or water and splashes as tiny droplets.

Static electricity by the falls. In 1871, S. H. Lockett, a professor of engineering at Louisiana University, said that electricity made from the mist (at Niagara Falls)

> *"might be used in producing grand and striking effects, thus adding another attractive feature to the sights at this wonderful place."*

He had observed that when the wind blew large amounts of mist to the Upper Suspension Bridge (it was a little closer to the falls than today's Rainbow Bridge), static electricity was produced, which he detected in a most unusual manner. According to the professor,

> *"while crossing the upper or New Suspension Bridge, I had occasion, while conversing with a friend, to point toward the Falls with my walking cane. As soon as I did so, I heard distinctly at the end of my cane a buzzing noise, like that made by electricity passing from a heavily charged battery to a sharp point rod. Repeating the experiment, the same noise was heard. I stopped several passers and tried their canes with the same result, except in one case, where there was no ferrule (metal cap or ring at the end) on the cane.*

I immediately supposed this might be an electrical phe-
nomenon and set to work to test the correctness of my suppo-
sition. I took a key and held it at arm's length toward the Falls
and heard the same sound. Finally, at dark I returned to the
bridge and pointed my cane in the air, and had the satisfaction
of seeing a clear, beautiful electric brush on its end. The best
point to observe this interesting and beautiful phenomenon is
in the middle of the bridge, and the cane must be at arm's
length, so that its end may be at some distance from any part
of the bridge. The success of the experiment seems to depend a
good deal on the direction of the wind and the amount of va-
por blown over the Bridge.

My explanation of the phenomenon is this: As Franklin
with his kite caught the lightning from the clouds of heaven,
so here from the Suspension Bridge, surrounded by the va-
pors of the mighty Falls, we may stand and gather on our
walking canes the electricity generated from the falling wa-
ters and contained in the floating mists."

The foam on the river below Niagara Falls. It is natural. It is calcium carbonate which has come out of solution or precipitated from water which evaporated when going over the falls. Mixed with the calcium carbonate are lignins and tannins from decaying algae. As the foam floats downstream, it redisolves in the water.

Animals going over Niagara Falls. Wild animals of all kinds, from small fish to moose and elk, have been going over the falls for thousands of years. Many of them survived going over the Horseshoe Falls, especially the fish, but very few, even fish, made it through the pile of rocks below the American and Bridal Veil Falls. On foggy nights, it was not uncommon for thousands of ducks, geese and swans to go over.

Strange weather. The year 1816 has been called "the year without a summer." Frost occurred every month. Ice formed an inch thick in May. Snow fell to a depth of three inches in June. Ice formed to a thickness of window glass on the 4th of July. Corn was so frozen in August that it was cut down and dried for fodder. It was possible to walk on ice to Goat Island and the Three Sisters Islands in May.

On June 29, 1884, a man slipped on a piece of ice in the gorge below Prospect Park. There was still ice left over from the previous winter.

Fishfalls and frogfalls. After a thunderstorm on July 13, 1927, a man in St. Catherines found a number of small fish all over his backyard.

In Niagara Falls, New York, on May 23, 1933, and in Niagara Falls, Ontario, on February 16, 1938, fish came down from the sky during storms.

On October 6, 1937, tiny frogs were seen falling from the sky during a storm near Clarendon, New York, and they were all alive after the fall.

"Sea serpents." A number of times, strange creatures have been seen in the Niagara River and Lake Ontario. On September 13, 1884, at 9 o'clock in the morning, according to the *Lockport Daily Union,*

> *"a monstrous sea serpent fifty feet in length with a head as big as a large barrel was seen by Dan McKim of Lockport, at the mouth of (the) Niagara River. He was out fishing in a boat and the sea serpent appeared on the top of the water twice, the latter time within 100 feet (31 meters) of his boat. Mr. McKim describes the monster as having eyes about four inches in diameter with red rings around them. It had tusks like a wild boar and two horns on its head. Its tail resembled that of a fish and was full five feet (1.5 meters) across. The serpent was seen by a soldier on guard at the fort (Fort Niagara) and by a party of fishermen on shore. Many fish nets have been destroyed at the mouth of the river this season, and it is now supposed to be the work of the serpent seen this morning."*

A similar serpent was seen on August 31, 1893 and August 9, 1895, in the Niagara River and Lake Ontario. Could the Loch Ness monster have a relative living in the Niagara Region?

Lewiston "Bigfoot?" From 1960 to 1980, people in Lewiston, New York, claimed to have seen as many as four creatures resembling the apelike Bigfoot or Sasquatch in local forests. One man said he photographed the monster. The existence of the creature(s) was never proven.

The unnatural lure of the Niagara Falls and rapids. According to Niagara Falls historian, Charles Mason Dow,

"in some cases the effect of the falling waters is so great as to inspire an almost uncontrollable desire to leap into the foaming tide. It is perhaps this power of the cataract to lure to self-destruction that the Indians tried to explain in their legend that the Falls demand four victims annually. Be the explanation what it may, this psychological effect of the Falls on certain temperaments is an interesting study."

In 1839, when Captain Frederick Marryat visited Niagara Falls, he remarked that, after staring at the falls for awhile, he

"felt a slight dizziness and creeping sensation come over me — that sensation arising from strong excitement, and the same, probably, that occasions the bird to fall into the jaws of the snake. This is a feeling which, if too long indulged in, becomes irresistible, and occasions a craving desire to leap into the flood of rushing waters. It increased upon me every minute; and retreating from the brink, I turned my eyes to the surrounding foliage, until the effect of the excitement had passed away."

Niagara's cedar trees. Once more common, they can be seen in the Niagara River Gorge and along the Niagara Escarpment. Before 1806, the only way to go down into the gorge by the American

Falls was by means of a large cedar tree. According to the late Niagara County historian, Clarence O. Lewis,

> *"early travelers tell of following a path from the Old French Landing (now Porter's Park) along the bank of the river to a spot below Prospect Point, near the end of what is now called Niagara street. Here a tall cedar tree had been made into a crude ladder, either by the Indians or the French, probably in the 1750's."*

The tree Lewis referred to could have been extremely old. According to Canadian botanist, Douglas Larson, cedars growing along the Niagara Escarpment and in parts of the gorge grow very slowly. A 1000-year-old tree may be only 8 inches (20 centimeters) in diameter!

Chapter 6:

Reflecting on Nature's Niagara

For over 300 years, many writers, painters, scientists, and photographers have labored to accurately describe the natural history and character of the Niagara Region, especially the Niagara Falls. Yet, it can be argued that not one of them has succeeded.

To clearly understand and explain nature, stimuli must be received through the senses of sight, hearing, smell, touch, and space. Words, drawings, photographs, audio recordings, movies, and videos do not stimulate the senses of smell, touch, and space. Only a real life experience can do that.

Obviously, it isn't always possible to experience a natural situation or object. That is when the imagination must be used to its fullest.

This chapter contains a selection of prose and poetry about the Niagara Region and places like it. Let the imagination soar!

"Early some morning,

> *Go to the shore above the American Rapids;*

Walk, letting the current direct you.

> *The stream quivers before becoming tumultuous;*

Splashing, churning, spraying, gurgling

> *Its way to the brink of the falls.*

Over the edge and into the misty abyss,

> *The water thunders and yields to gravity.*

No bolts of lightning precede the sound,

> *But it creates the same fear and respect*

As a great storm on the sea.

> *Fleeing the chaos below,*

Air rushes up and swirls around the scene.

> *In the sky are soaring ring-billed gulls*

Eerily calling out to each other."

Paul Gromosiak, 2000

"From Lake Erie to the great plunge, the river flows in a rapid down-grade, and as it reaches the falls, it is not so much a river as a sea whose torrents surge into the gaping mouth of a chasm. The cataract is split into two branches, and bends in the form of a horse-shoe. Between the two falls an island juts out, hollow underneath, and hanging with all its trees over the chaos of the waves. The mass of water hurtling down in the south curves into a vast cylinder, then straightens into a snowy sheet, sparkling iridescent in the sunlight. The eastern branch falls in dismal gloom, calling to mind some downpour of the great flood. A thousand rainbows arch and intersect with the abyss. As it strikes the shuddering rock, the water bounds back in foaming whirlpools, which drift up over the forest like the smoke of some vast conflagration. The scene is ornate with pine and wild walnut trees and rocks carved out in weird shapes. Eagles, drawn by air currents, spiral down into the depths of the chasm, and wolverines dangle by their supple tails from the ends of low-hanging branches, snatching the shattered corpses of elk and bears out of the abyss."

Francois Rene de Chateaubriand, 1801

"Describe it! Who can ere describe
The lightning's flash — the Thunder's roll.
Say what is Life, or what is Death,
Or paint the portrait of the Soul?"

David Paul Brown, 1854

"There may be taller cataracts in Africa, South America, and even elsewhere in New York State, but the sheer size and tremendous volume of Niagara are unsurpassed. Contrary to popular opinion, Niagara Falls is not listed as one of the Seven Wonders of the World. Still these falls are a wonder. It is the combination of height and volume that makes them so beautiful and wondrous."

Deborah Williams, 1995

"Niagara the great, the free, old Erie's swift discharger,

Ontario bids welcome to thy foaming, gushing waters,

That freshly fill her yawning caves, and nourish all her daughters."

Joseph John Gurney, 1841

"M. Joncaire [the Frenchman in charge of the goods shipped between Lakes Erie and Ontario in the first half of the 18th century] and all others declared that the falls occasionally made louder racket than at other times. When its roar was unusually strong in any direction, it was said infallibly to indicate rain and bad weather. This was the reason, it was claimed, why the Indians of the neighborhood were able to prophecy the weather so accurately."

Peter Kalm, 1750

"As long as I live, I'll hear waterfalls and birds and winds sing. I'll interpret the rocks, learn the language of flood, storm, and avalanche. I'll acquaint myself with the glaciers and wild gardens, and get as near the heart of the world as I can."

John Muir

About the Author

Paul Gromosiak, one of the region's most respected Niagara Falls historians, takes great pride in being a life-long Western New Yorker. Born in 1942 in Niagara Falls, New York, Paul's fascination with the Mighty Niagara was sparked at home. His father would often tell him stories about early life on the Niagara Frontier. Paul has been researching Niagara's natural and human past ever since, authoring six books that focus on different aspects of the falls.

When people want to know about the Falls, they look to Gromosiak. He is frequently interviewed by both local and national media, appearing on CBS and in a PBS documentary called *Fading in the Mist*. Canada's weekly newsmagazine MacLean's even interviewed him about the custom of honeymooning at the Falls.

Gromosiak's articles have appeared in the *Buffalo News*, the *Niagara Gazette* and other publications. His books include: *Niagara Falls Q & A, Answers to the 100 Most Common Questions about Niagara Falls, Soaring Gulls and Bowing Trees: The History of the Islands Above the Falls, Zany Niagara: The Funny Things People Say About Niagara Falls* and *Water Over the Falls: 101 of the Most Memorable Events at Niagara Falls*.

Birth of a Publishing Firm

The Buffalo region's most innovative publishing company celebrated its 16th anniversary in 2000 by hitting a benchmark that most regional publishing houses only dream about.

Since its inception, Western New York Wares Inc. has moved more than 120,000 books and games into homes, schools and libraries across the nation. Not bad for a company that sprouted its roots in trivial turf!

The year was 1984 and the trivia craze was taking the nation by storm. As Buffalo journalist Brian Meyer played "the other trivia game" with friends in his North Buffalo living room, he came up with the notion of creating a local game that tested players' knowledge about the people, places and events in their hometown. Western New York Trivia Quotient hit store shelves several months later, selling out its first edition in only six weeks. The newest edition is still available.

A year later, Meyer compiled a book of quotations that chronicled the feisty reign of Mayor Jimmy Griffin. A follow-up volume was published eight years later, Griffin's last year in office.

Meyer, a business reporter for the *Buffalo News*, spent nearly 16 years at WBEN Radio where he served as managing editor. During his tenure, he won more state and regional awards than any other radio reporter in Western New York.

As founder and president of Western New York Wares Inc., Meyer was also methodically building his innovative publishing company. He began collaborating with local authors, artists and photographers on a variety of book projects.

By 2000, the region's premier publisher of local books and games had nearly 50 products in its catalog.

Meyer is a graduate of the Marquette University College of Journalism, St. Joseph's Collegiate Institute and Buffalo Public School # 56. He teaches communications courses at Buffalo State College and Medaille College. He enjoys spending weekends hiking and canoeing at his cottage at Rushford Lake in Allegany County.

Internet Site Focuses on Local History, Sports, Weather and Tourist Attractions

www.wnybooks.com

Our unique web site is a treasure trove of information for those who enjoy learning about the people, places and events that have shaped Western New York.

The site showcases full-color photography some of the region's most respected shutterbugs and literary passages from many best-selling regional books. The works of more than 30 local authors, photographers and game inventors are included.

Browsers will enjoy meandering through the many "departments" of our cyberspace bookstore:

Niagara Falls: The history and magnetism of this natural wonder spring to life on our web site. Learn more about daredevils who defied the Mighty Niagara, humorous happenings and unusual historical facts.

Nature: Enjoy a stunning visual celebration of Western New York's natural treasures. Full color photographs and vividly written descriptions will spur many adventurers to explore these wonders firsthand.

Ghosts/Supernatural: East Aurora author Mason Winfield shares some "ghostly" insights into paranormal happenings in Western New York.

Weather: Channel 7 weather guru Tom Jolls chronicles many of the most memorable, humorous and dramatic tales about Buffalo's four seasons.

Sports: Buffalo Bills photographs spring to life, courtesy of respected photographer Robert L. Smith. Savor some of the greatest moments in football history as the chief photographer for the Bills takes fans on a visual roller coaster road that spans three decades.

The Internet site also showcases regional books for children, architectural guides and walking tours.

www.wnybooks.com

94

Other Books Distributed by Western New York Wares, Inc.

Niagara Falls Q & A: Answers to the 100 Most Common Questions About Niagara Falls — Author Paul Gromosiak spent four summers chatting with 40,000 Falls tourists. This invaluable guide answers the most commonly asked questions.
ISBN: 0-9620314-8-8   **$4.50**

Daring Niagara: 50 Death-Defying Stunts at the Falls — Paul Gromosiak pens a heart-stopping adventure about those who barreled, boated, even bicycled to fame. The book includes vintage photographs.
ISBN: 1-879201-23-2   **$6.95**

Water Over the Falls: 101 of the Most Memorable Events at Niagara Falls — Daredevils who defied the Mighty Niagara, tragic rock slides and heroic rescues. More than 100 true-to-life tales are vividly recounted by noted local historian Paul Gromosiak.
ISBN: 1-879201-16-X   **$5.95**

Zany Niagara: The Funny Things People Say About Niagara Falls — A fun-filled tour of humorous happenings and historical oddities. Penned by Paul Gromosiak and illustrated by John Hardiman.
ISBN: 1-879201-06-2   **$4.95**

Exploring Niagara: The Complete Guide to Niagara Falls and Vicinity — Filled with 77 spectacular full color photos, the guide includes dozens of tours of wineries, canals, waterfalls, mansions and forests. Authors Hans and Allyson Tammemagi also chronicle the history which has shaped our region.
ISBN: 0-9681815-0-3   **$14.25**

Victorian Buffalo: Images from the Buffalo and Erie County Public Library — Get a glimpse of Buffalo as it looked in the 19th century by viewing this unique collection of steel engravings, woodcuts, lithography and other forms of nonphotographic art. Author Cynthia VanNess has selected scenes that showcase everyday life as well as views of historic structures created by luminaries like Frank Lloyd Wright, Louis Sullivan and E. B. Green.
ISBN: 1-879201-30-5   **$12.95**

Shadows of the Western Door — Haunted Sites and Ancient Mysteries of Upstate New York — A supernatural safari across Western New York. Guided by the insights of modern research, author Mason Winfield pens a colorful, provocative and electrifying study of the paranormal.
ISBN: 1-879201-22-4   **$12.95**

A Ghosthunter's Journal: Tales of the Supernatural and the Strange in Upstate New York — Telepathic stalkers, visionary cults and a dozen other fictional tales by Mason Winfield.
ISBN: 1-879201-29-1   **$12.95**

John D. Larkin: A Business Pioneer — The riveting story of a Buffalo man who built a small soap manufacturing outfit into one of the largest mail order houses in the nation. Daniel I. Larkin, a grandson of John D. Larkin, has penned a book that reflects the American dream at its best.
ISBN: 0-9619697-1-7   **$14.95**

Great Lake Effects: Buffalo Beyond Winter and Wings — The region's most unique cookbook, compiled by the Junior League of Buffalo. A delectable collection of 145 recipes, served up in a hardcover book rich with historical facts about the region.
ISBN: 0-9655935-0-9   **$18.95**

Western New York Weather Guide — Readers won't want any "winterup-tions" as they breeze through this lively book that focuses on Buffalo's four seasons. Penned by Channel 7 weather guru Tom Jolls with assistance from Brian Meyer and Joseph Van Meer, this guide focuses on humorous and historic weather events over the past century.
ISBN: 1-879201-18-1   **$7.95**

A View Through the Lens of Robert L. Smith: Buffalo Bills Photos — Bills owner Ralph Wilson says the 444 photos in this unique collection "provide enjoyment and touches of nostalgia I wouldn't trade for a first round draft choice." This eye-grabbing photographic journey chronicles the team's ups and downs from its inception in 1960 to the end of the Jim Kelly era.
ISBN: 1-879201-17-8   **$26.95**

Beyond Buffalo: A Photographic Journey and Guide to the Secret Natural Wonders of our Region — Full-color photographs and informative vignettes showcase 30 remarkable sites in Western New York. Author David Lawrence Reade includes complete directions and tips for enjoying each site.
ISBN: *1-879201-19-4* **$19.95**

Buffalo Treasures: A Downtown Walking Guide — Readers are led on a fascinating tour of 25 major buildings. A user-friendly map and dozens of photos and illustrations supplement a text written by Jan Sheridan.
ISBN: *1-879201-15-1* **$4.95**

Church Tales of the Niagara Frontier: Legends, History & Architecture — This first-of-a-kind book traces the rich history and folklore of the region through accounts of 60 area churches and places of worship. Written by Austin M. Fox and illustrated by Lawrence McIntyre.
ISBN: *1-879201-13-5* **$14.95**

Buffalo's Waterfront: A Guidebook — Edited by Tim Tielman, this 72-page guide showcases more than 100 shoreline sites. The work includes a special fold-out map. Published by the Preservation Coalition of Erie County.
ISBN: *1-879201-00-3* **$5.95**

The World According to Griffin: The End of an Era — Compiled by veteran broadcast journalist Brian Meyer, this almanac includes hundreds of "Griffinisms" from one of the most feisty mayors in Buffalo history.
ISBN: *1-879201-11-9* **$5.95**

The A-to-Z Bus Tour of Buffalo (and Beyond) — This coloring book takes youngsters on an exciting alphabetical tour of Western New York. Seven-year-old Christian Ratzel co-authored the book with Brian Meyer. Grand Island artist Anna Finkel illustrated it.
ISBN: *1-879201-10-0* **$3.50**

Buffalo City Hall: Americanesque Masterpiece — Local Historian John Conlin has penned this authoritative guide which chronicles the history and architectural significance of this regional icon.
ISBN: *1-879201-14-3* **$5.95**

Buffalo Chips: The Book — More than 100 rib-tickling entrees from local cartoonist Tom Stratton.
ISBN: *0-9620314-3-7* **$4.95**

Quotable Cuomo: The Mario Years — An offbeat almanac of political quotes and anecdotes compiled by Mary Murray and Brian Meyer.
ISBN: *1-879201-03-0* **$5.95**

Buffalo's Brush With the Arts: From Huck Finn to Murphy Brown — A fascinating armchair journey behind the manuscripts and million dollar book deals, highlighting the Niagara Frontier's connection to many creative geniuses. Authored by Joe Marren, the 112-page softcover book contains more than 20 photographs from the Courier-Express Collection.
ISBN: *1-879201-24-0* **$7.95**

Hometown Heroes: Western New Yorkers in Desert Storm — (Brian Meyer and Tom Connolly)
ISBN: *1-879201-04-6* **$5.95**

Buffalo: A Bulls Eye View — An offbeat almanac of local anecdotes.
ISBN: *0-6816410-5-3* **$4.95**

Please include 8% sales tax and $2 for shipping.
Or write for a catalog of all regional books and games:
Western New York Wares Inc.
Attention: Brian Meyer
P.O. Box 733, Ellicott Station
Buffalo, New York 14205

Visit our internet site: www.wnybooks.com

96

NATURAL THINGS TO DO
AFTER SENSING THE
WONDER OF THE FALLS:

A. HIKING
B. BIRDWATCHING
C. OBSERVING FALL FOLIAGE
D. VIEWING WINTER SCENERY

THE NIAGARA FA

N

SCALE

0   1 MILE

0   1   2 KILOMETERS

HORSESHOE OR CANADIAN FALLS

MAID OF THE MIST POOL

TABLE ROCK

O N T A R I O

A,B,C,D

DUFFERIN
ISLANDS
A,B,C,D

OLD RIVER SHORELINE

UPPER

A,B,C,D

RAINBOW
BRIDGE

HUBBARD POINT
(FALLS BEGAN
TO DECREASE
IN HEIGHT 3500BP)

AMERICAN
FALLS

EDDY BA

GOAT
ISLAND
A,B,
C,D

OLD RIVER
SHORELINE

GREAT

A,B,C,D

CANADIAN
RAPIDS

THREE
SISTERS
ISLANDS
A,B,C,D

GORGE

A,B,C,D

PROSPECT
POINT
A,B,C,D

A,B,C,D

WHIRLPOOL RA

DIVIDING OF
THE WATERS

AMERICAN
RAPIDS

SCHOELLKOPF
GEOLOGICAL
MUSEUM

GORGE

WHERE ST. DAVID'S FALLS
WAS BURIED UNTIL 4000 BP

WHIRLPOOL RAPIDS
BRIDGE

A,B,C,D

OLD LAKE
SHORELINE

UPPER NIAGARA RIVER

NIAGARA ISLAND (IT CEASED
BEING AN ISLAND WHEN LAKE
TONAWANDA DRAINED OFF
3500 BP)

DRY BED OF LAKE TONAWANDA

N E W   YO